SCHOLASTIC

AF513223

The WORLD Around Us 3

Teacher's Manual

Published by Scholastic India Pvt. Ltd.
A subsidiary of Scholastic Inc., New York, 10012 (USA).
Publishers since 1920, with international operations in Canada, Australia, New Zealand, the United Kingdom, India, and Hong Kong.

For information regarding permission, write to:
Scholastic India Pvt. Ltd.
A-27, Ground Floor, Sigma Centre
Infocity-1, Sector 34, Gurgaon-122001 (India)

First edition: May 2025

ISBN-13: 978-81-8477-370-5

Printed at : Shiv Shakti Printing & Trading Co., Haryana

Contents

Part I: Social Studies

Lesson 1	The Beginning of Time	6
Lesson 2	Maps and Directions	10
Lesson 3	Continents and Oceans	13
Lesson 4	India—Physical	16
Lesson 5	India—Political	19
Lesson 6	India—Food and Clothing	22
Lesson 7	Indian Culture and Traditions	25
Lesson 8	National Symbols and Emblem	29
Lesson 9	Important Cities of India	32

Part II: Science

Lesson 10	Living and Non-living Things	39
Lesson 11	Parts of a Plant	42
Lesson 12	Animals	46
Lesson 13	Birds	49
Lesson 14	The Human Body	52
Lesson 15	Food	56
Lesson 16	The Universe and the Solar System	59
Lesson 17	Natural Resources	63
Lesson 18	Matter and Its Properties	67
Lesson 19	Energy and Forces	69
Worksheets: Answers		72

PART I: SOCIAL STUDIES

Lesson 1 The Beginning of Time

Before you begin

Show the class, pictures of some famous people as children, in their youth and their most recent pictures. (You may find these pictures on the internet, in biographies or autobiographies of these personalities.) You could also share with the class pictures of yourself when you were a child. Discuss with the class how we age as time goes by.

Ask them to discuss how we get information about something that existed many years ago. Help them articulate for themselves the various sources of information like fossils, ancient monuments, paintings, tools, jewellery, etc.

Objectives

This chapter provides the students with a broad overview of what is meant by history. The main topics discussed in this lesson are:

- history—its study and sources.
- timelines.
- definition of CE and BCE.
- the history of early humans—the use of tools, discovery of fire, early human settlements, early transport and invention of the wheel.

  While discussing timelines, and especially the concept of how years are counted, give the students plenty of examples so that they are comfortable about the concept of BCE and CE. Draw diagrams to help reinforce the concepts.

  Explore: collect pictures and make a family tree Students will bring the pictures of family members and make a family tree.

  Learn More: use encyclopedia
  Take the children to library to find information. Teach how to use an encyclopedia.

Learn More:

- ➢ If possible, screen a documentary about early humans and how they evolved.

OR

- ➢ If your city/town has a museum of natural sciences, take the students for a field trip there. Help them observe the exhibits on early humans, the tools they used, how humans came to settle in communities, early pottery and jewellery. Please inform the parents in advance about the excursion and make sure they have adequate water, some dry snacks and their identity cards with them before setting off on the field trip.

Circle Time: importance of wheel

Uses of wheel for humans should be discussed. Create scenarios of modern life without wheel and ask the students to identify the difficulties in the situation.

Additional activities

- You could also show the students pictures of early human dwellings, pottery, jewellery and artifacts found in early human settlements like the Indus Valley Civilisation
- and Mesopotamia. These pictures can be easily found in encyclopedias, books on early human civilisation and on the Internet.
- To clarify the concept of the timeline and especially how time is measured in CE and BCE, draw a timeline on the board, indicating CE and BCE. Indicate the centuries on this timeline. Now call out important events in history and the time when these incidents took place and ask the students, by rotation, to come and mark the events on the timeline.

Answers

1. Use the clues in the brackets to unscramble these words.

a. SRIOTHY (the study of the past) (History)
b. AANRLECD (used to see the year/dates) (Calendar)
c. IIEENMTL (the sequence of events) (Timeline)
d. SEAVC (early humans lived here) (Caves)
e. IERF (used by early humans to stay warm and cook) (Fire)
f. EEHWL (its invention was the turning point in human history) (Wheel)

2. Write T for true and F for false.

a. The earliest human remains have been found in Asia. False
b. The year of the birth of Jesus Christ is taken to be zero. True
c. The first year after Christ was born is written as 2 CE. False
d. The scientific name for human beings is Homo sapiens. True

e. Early humans used a language to communicate with each other. False

f. Animals made it easier for humans to transport goods. True

3. Answer the following questions.

a. What is a timeline?

Timeline is a tool to understand what happened in the past and when. It shows the sequence of events in the past.

b. How do we measure the years before the birth of Jesus Christ? The year of Birth of Jesus Christ is taken as year zero. We measure the years before the birth of Christ by counting backwards from the year zero. So, the year just before Christ was born is written as 1 BCE (Before Christian Era/Before Common Era).

c. What kinds of tools were used by early humans? What materials did they use to make these tools?

- Early humans used sharp tools to dig out roots and to kill animals for food.
- These tools were made up of stones, bones and wood.
- They used to develop a sharp edge by striking one stone against the other.
- They learnt to tie sharp stones to sticks and used them as spears.
- They also learnt to use make and use tools for fishing, digging and sewing.
- As many stone tools were used during this period, it is referred to as the Stone Age.

d. What did early humans use fire for? What do modern humans use fire for?

Early humans used fire

- to keep warm
- to keep away the wild animals.

Early humans discovered that fire could be used to cook food and that food tasted better when cooked.

Modern humans use fire for

- cooking,
- keeping warm,
- transportation (steam engine),
- manufacturing (pottery, metals, plastics and many other products)

e. What would you do to save yourself from heat and cold if you were living in the Stone Age?
We would save ourselves from cold by wearing the fur and skin of animals.
We would use stone tools to roughly sew together pieces of fur, animal skins and leaves to make clothes.
To save ourselves from heat, we would stay in shaded areas and take a bath with water frequently.

f. How has the invention of the wheel transformed human life?
The invention of the wheel brought change the way of doing things. – transportation, in industry, for pottery.
- It is used to carry goods from one place to another.
- It was used to go from one place to another.
- It is used by a potter to make pottery easily
- It is used in all modes of transportation.
- It is used in many machines used in industries.

4. Critical Thinking.

a. Why did early humans use hand movements to communicate?
Early humans did not have a language of communication, so they used hand movements to talk to each other.

b. Why did early humans settle down?
Once the early humans started to grow their own food, they had to settle down in one place in order to look after the plants. They chose areas near rivers, where the land was suitable for farming. Rivers also provided water for irrigating crops.

5. Social Emotional Skills

Discuss how easy our lives are now, compared to the lives of early humans.
Life of early humans was very difficult.
They used tools for hunting, lived in caves and forests and moved from place to place in small groups in search of food.
They covered themselves with leaves or skins of animals.
Teacher can have a discussion on how life has become easy.
Accept all appropriate answers.

6. Creativity:

Use soft clay to try and make the face of an early human.

Lesson 2 Maps and Directions

Before you begin

Start the lesson by first showing the students a map, a compass and a globe. Have them look at these carefully and ask them to tell you how they are useful to us.

While discussing maps, show the students an atlas to help them recognise the fact that there can be many different types of maps—physical and political. Also, as an exercise to help the students see the importance of a map, have them draw a map of how they reach from the school gate to their classroom.

Objectives

This chapter introduces the student to the basics of maps and directions. The main topics covered in this lesson are:

- the definition of a map.
- the use of a globe.
- the four cardinal directions and the four intermediate directions.
- reading maps.

Explore: route from home to school
Students will draw the sketch and mark the landmarks.
Learn More: locate your country on a globe Get a globe and a map of the world to class. Help students identify the county and city in which they live on both.

Learn More:
This activity will help to familiarise the students with using a compass to tell directions. Bring a compass to class. Divide the class into four groups and assign each group a classroom wall. This now becomes 'their' wall. Now work with each group in turns. Have one group at a time circle you and look at the compass to find out the direction 'their' wall faces.
Once the direction has been determined ask each group to make a colourful label indicating the direction 'their' wall faces. Stick these labels on the respective walls.

Additional activities

- An activity that will help reinforce map reading skills among the students is to organise a treasure hunt. Divide the class into pairs. Post clues on big pieces of chart papers like 'go west from the see-saw', or 'the next clue is posted on the south side of the school auditorium', etc., across the school. All the hints should use the cardinal directions. The 'treasure' could be a bag of sweets or a bar of chocolate. The treasure hunt can be as easy or complicated as you want it to be.
- Another fun activity that can be played in class is to locate a secret place on a map. For this game, hang a big world map in class. Every child has to come up to the map in turns and guess the secret place you are thinking about. Ask the child to point on any random place on the world map. Now, following your instructions, the child has to locate the place you are thinking of. So you can give instructions like 'go north till you see the Himalayas', 'go east till you see the Brahmaputra River', 'go south of Dispur', etc.

Answers

1. Study the given map carefully.

Now colour each compass rose to show the correct direction.

a. In what direction is the Town Hall from the Hospital?	North
b. On which corner is the Supermarket?	South East
c. On which corner is the Hospital?	South West
d. You ran out of money at the Supermarket. In which direction should you go if you need to get money from the Bank?	North
e. In which direction would you go if you wanted to go from the Supermarket to the Town Hall?	North West

2. Match the following.

a. The direction in which the Sun sets — iii. West

b. Chennai is in this part of India — v. South

c. This rises in the East iv. Sun
d. Between South and West is this direction ii. South West
e. This is a navigational tool to find directions i. Compass

3. Answer the following questions.

a. What is a globe?
A model of the Earth is known as a globe. It shows us the Earth as a whole. We can rotate the globe to see the different places on Earth.

b. When do we use a compass?
We use a compass when we want to find direction. A compass always points to magnetic North of the earth. Using North, we can find the other directions.

c. What is an atlas?
A book of maps is called an atlas.

d. What is the difference between a globe and a map?

Map	Globe
A map is a drawing or a sketch of an area.	A model of the Earth is known as a globe.
A map can be of a small neighbourhood or it can show a large area or a country.	It shows us the Earth as a whole.

e. What difficulties will you face if you do not have a map while travelling?
If we do not have a map while travelling:
- we will not be able to know how far are we from our destination
- we will not be able to identify where we have reached
- we will not be able to find the correct route to destination
- we may get lost or will spend more time in reaching destination

f. How can a compass help sailors who are lost at sea?
A compass gives the sailors a fixed direction to the magnetic north pole. Once the north is known, the sailor can choose a direction in which to go. If he follows the direction for a specific distance he can reach his destination.

4. **Critical Thinking:**

a. Why does a globe rotate?

Globe is a model of the earth. Earth rotates around its axis every 24 hours.

b. Why do we need maps?

A map is a drawing of an area.

Depending on the kind of map, it shows us the position of

- streets and important places
- towns, cities, village, districts
- countries, continents
- rivers, lakes
- mountains, seas, oceans

Using a map we can know about the area.

5. **Social Emotional Skills:**

Should we differentiate between people on the basis of the countries they live in? Discuss.

Students will provide answers. Accept appropriate answers. Teacher should focus on similarity between all human beings. Customs, traditions, dress, languages and food may be different for people of different countries but human beings are similar.

6. **Creativity:**

Draw a map of your school building on a chart paper. Show the locations and directions of the Library, Laboratory, Admin Office, Canteen and your classroom from the Principal's office.

Lesson 3 Continents and Oceans

Before you begin

Before starting the lesson in class, arrange a large world map to be put up in class or get a large-size globe to class. Ask the students to list the names of the continents they have heard of. In case some children mention the names of countries instead, show them where that country is located on the map/globe and which continent it is a part of. This will help to give the students an understanding that a continent is a very large mass of land which is further subdivided into countries.

Objectives

This chapter will educate the students about:

- the shape of the earth.
- definition of horizon.
- the seven continents.
- the five oceans.
- the difference between an ocean and a sea.
- definition of an island and an archipelago.

Explore: find names of any four countries

Each student will identify the countries. Ask the students to locate them on globe/world map.

Circle Time: play ladder game

Play the game as mentioned in the student book. Ensure participation by all students.

Learn More: Use an atlas to find an archipelago in the Indian Ocean

Encourage the students to read the atlas and find an archipelago in the Indian Ocean on their own.

Additional activities

- ➢ Divide the class into twelve groups. Assign each group a continent or an ocean. Ask them to find out four very interesting facts about their continent/ocean. Encourage the children to use encyclopedias, the internet or the school library to find the information. Each group can present these interesting facts either in the form of a chart or make a verbal presentation in class.
- ➢ Once the students are familiar with the names of the continents and countries, play a word ladder game in class. You can either divide the class into two groups or make this an individual game. The first group/student has to say the name of a continent or country that starts with the letter A. The next group/student has to say the name of a continent/country which starts with the last alphabet of the previous continent/country's name. The word ladder can go on till all the names are exhausted.

Answers

1. Find the names of the continents in the word grid.

North America – 2nd row

Africa – 4th row
Antarctica – 4th column
Asia – 6th column
Europe – 8th column
Australia – 12th column
South America – Diagonally up from last row, first column

2. Write T for true and F for false.

a. People always believed that the Earth was flat. False (only in ancient times)

b. Magellan set out with a fleet of ships from India. False

c. Magellan's sailors sailed around the Earth, proving that it was round. True

d. Our country is in the African continent. False

e. Australia is the smallest continent. True

3. Answer the following questions.

a. What is the horizon?
The horizon is the circular line at which the sky and the Earth appear to meet. If we stand on a flat plain the horizon appears to be at the same distance in every direction.

b. How many oceans are there in the world? Name them. There are five oceans in the world. These are:
Arctic Ocean Atlantic Ocean Indian Ocean Pacific Ocean Southern Ocean

c. Which continent is India a part of? Asia

d. What is an archipelago?
A group of islands located close to one another is called an archipelago.

e. What would happen if there are more continents and fewer oceans on Earth?

- temperatures would rise
- climate would be very different
- atmosphere would have less oxygen
- life would not be possible

f. How advantageous is it for a country to be surrounded by seas?

Advantages

- natural barrier of sea against invaders

- good sea life
- good beaches
- Attracts tourists

Disadvantages

- lot of things have to be imported
- most do not have a large population
- face the effects of climate changes as sea level are increasing

4. Critical Thinking:

a. Even if we travel too far, we will not fall off the edge of the Earth. Why?
Earth is round so we will not fall of the edge of the earth.

b. Why does the horizon appear to be at the same distance in every direction?
Our eyes can see up to same distance in all directions.

5. Social Emotional Skills:

The world is one family. Discuss.
Students can discuss using following ideas:
We are on one planet that revolves around the sun. Human beings for all counties are more similar than different
The resources of earth are for all humanity.
Teacher can use the phrase "Vasudhaiva Kutumbakam" and mention that this is mentioned in Upanishads (ancient Indian scriptures).

6. Creativity:

Take a world map. Colour and label the seven continents and cut them out. Make a globe using these cuttings and a big ball.

Lesson 4 India—Physical

Before you begin

Hang a big physical map of India in the classroom. Ask the children to observe it carefully and then play a small game to help them remember the names of important physical features of India. Call out the alphabet starting with the letter 'A'. Ask the students to call out the name of any physical feature starting with the letter you call out. List these on the class board. Prompt them with a few clues like 'it is a very tall mountain range starting with the letter H'; 'it is a big ocean to the south of India and it starts with the letter I', etc.

Objectives

This chapter seeks to provide the students with comprehensive information about India's important physical features, namely:

- the northern mountains.
- the northern plains.
- the Thar Desert.
- the Deccan Plateau and the Ghats.
- the coastal regions.
- the islands.

Explore: Colours used to show physical features on map
Mountains: Brown
Forests: Green
Rivers: Blue
Desert: Yellow

Explore: first person to climb Mount Everest
Edmund Hillary

Learn More: Origin of River Ganges
The students need to find where the River Ganga originates. Encourage them to look up an encyclopedia or use the internet to find this information.

Learn More: difference between Eastern and Western Ghats
Ask the students to prepare a chart on their findings.

Learn more: use atlas to find capitals
Bring an atlas to the class and ask the students to identify the capitals of Andaman and Nicobar Islands and Lakshadweep.

Additional activities

➢ Draw a large map of India or hang a big blank map of India in class. Make labels for all the important physical features discussed in class. Stick some adhesive tape behind each label. Now, chose students randomly from the class to come and stick the labels in the appropriate places. In case a student makes a mistake, prompt him/

her to stick the label in the correct place by giving instructions such as 'a little north', or 'more to the west', etc. This will also reinforce the concept of cardinal directions.

- Divide the class into teams and organise a quiz on the physical features of India. You could ask questions like 'name the tallest mountain peak in India', 'which river starting with the letter G' flows through the Deccan Plateau', etc.

Answers

1. Unscramble the letters to form words related to India's physical features.

a. YASMIHLAA ______________________ Himalaya

b. HTAR SDEETR ____________________ Thar Desert

c. NWEETRS HGAST _______________ Western Ghats

d. RVRIE AGNGA ___________________ River Ganga

e. CADECN TEPLAUA _____________ Deccan Plateau

2. Write T for true and F for false.

a. In India, the highest peaks are found in the plateaus. False

b. The Indus river originates in the Himalayas. True

c. The eastern coastal plains are broader than the western coastal plains. True

d. The Andaman Islands are in the Bay of Bengal. True

e. The Thar Desert is very densely populated because of its easy living conditions. False

3. Answer the following questions.

a. What is a peninsula?
A peninsula is a large piece of land jutting out into the sea. It is surrounded by large water bodies on three sides.

b. Name some rivers that start in the Himalayas.
The Ganga, the Yamuna, the Indus and the Brahmputra

c. Which three large water bodies surround India?
Bay of Bengal, Arabian Sea and Indian Ocean

d. On a physical map of India, mark the following. To be done on map.

e. Describe the advantages of having the Himalayas as the northern boundary of India.
They provide a natural barrier against cold winds from north.
They provide a security barrier in the north

They are covered with snow that melts and are a source of many rives.
Himalayas have a large variety of plants and animal species which are useful.

f. What is the source of water for rivers? Melting of snow in the Himalayas. Rain water is the source for rivers in most other parts of India.
Some rivers may be from a natural spring (Ground water coming out).

4. Critical Thinking:

a. The Thar Desert is not very densely populated. Why is it so?
Thar Desert experiences hot, dry summers and cold winters. The population in this region is very sparse as it is difficult to live in such extreme conditions.

b. Why are the northern plains very fertile?
Northern plains are flatlands with many rivers flowing through them. The rivers bring with them a fine soil known as silt, which makes the northern plains very fertile and suitable for cultivation.

5. Social Emotional Skills:

Why do we compare rivers to mothers? Discuss.
Topics to be discussed:
Rivers bring water that is essential for humans. River bring fine soil that makes land fertile.
Rivers are a source of transportation. Rivers nurture us as a mother.

6. Creativity:

Work in groups and create a poster displaying an advertisement for a holiday destination in the mountains or by the sea.

Lesson 5 India—Political

Before you begin

Display a big political map of India in class. Ask the students to observe it carefully. Now have a quiz in class and ask the children to name all the states of India in alphabetical order. List them on the class board. See if they can list all the states.

Objectives

This chapter seeks to provide the students with a comprehensive overview of:

- the water bodies surrounding India.
- India's neighbours.
- structure of government in India.
- states, union territories and their capitals.

Explore: identify countries and locate on globe Ask the students to identify the countries and locate them on globe.

Learn More: locate capitals of India's neighbours
Student will have to locate the capitals in the atlas.
Learn More: name state, capital and Chief Minister Students have to be aware of the state/UT where they live. Name the state, capital and chief minister of the state/UT.

Additional activities

- ➢ Divide the class into teams. Conduct a quiz on the capitals of the states and union territories.
- ➢ Draw a big blank political map of India. Ask the students to come up to the map in turns and write the names of states in the appropriate places as you call them out.

Answers

1. Draw lines to match the states with their capitals.

a.	Uttar Pradesh •	• Lucknow
b.	Punjab •	• Chandigarh
c.	Goa •	• Panaji
d.	Mizoram •	• Aizwal
e.	Karnataka •	• Bengaluru
f.	Odisha •	• Bhubaneshwar
g.	West Bengal •	• Kolkata

2. Fill in the blanks to complete the sentences.

a. India's national language is ____________ Hindi

b. The separate India from the rest of Asia.____________ Himalayas

c. India has ____________union territories. Seven

d. India has ____________states. Twenty Nine

e. India is located in the continent of ____________. Asia

3. Answer the following questions.

a. Name India's neighbours.
Pakistan, Nepal, China, Bangladesh, Bhutan, Sri Lanka, Myanmar, Afghanistan

b. Name the largest and the smallest union territories in India.
Largest – Andaman and Nicobar Islands Smallest – Lakshadweep

c. Where is the central government located?
New Delhi

d. Label your state and its neighbouring states on a blank political map of India.
To be done by students.

e. What is the difference between a state and a union territory?
Each state has a state government that looks after the well-being of all the people living in the state.
Union territories come directly under the control of central government.

f. It is an advantage that India is divided into states. Explain.
India is a large country, it is difficult for the central government to look after the needs of such a large population by itself. Each state has a state government that looks after the well-being of all the people living in the state. The Governor, Chief Minister, other ministers and senior government officers of the state reside in the state capital.
Government of each State is able to promote their own languages, customs and traditions.

4. Critical Thinking:

a. The Himalayas are a natural boundary separating India from other countries. Explain.
They provide a security barrier in the north. The difficult terrain of the Himalayas make is difficult for people to travel across them.

b. Why does India have many regional languages despite having two official languages?
India is a large and diverse country. Different languages are spoken in different parts of the country. Less than half of the

population of India can understand the two official languages. Each state has defined official languages for their state.

5. **Social Emotional Skills:**
   Find out different aspects of the culture of the state you belong to. Discuss in the class.
   Ask students to find information about the culture of the state they belong to. Discuss in class.

6. **Creativity:**
   Which states will you travel across if you go from Delhi to Bengaluru by train? You can use the Internet or an atlas to find this information.
   Colour all these states on a blank political map of India.

Lesson 6 India—Food and Clothing

Before you begin

This is an excellent chapter to help students learn about the different states of India and gain an understanding of the diversity to be found in their own classroom. Ask the students to find out from their parents the state they originally belong to and the states their parents have come from. Ask the class to share this information and any specific information they might have about a particular state.

Objectives

This chapter seeks to acquaint the students to the diversity that exists within India. In particular, the chapter focuses on:

- diversity in food habits across the country.
- the different food items found in different parts of the country.
- the influence of climate on the type of clothing worn in a region.
- diversity in clothing across the country.

Explore: staple food of the state
Students have to know about the staple food of their state. They should bring it in lunch and share with the class.
Learn More: find national fruit of any five countries Students

have find out about the national fruit of 5 countries and share the findings with the class.

Circle Time: favourite sweet

Ask all students to mention their favourite sweets. Count the number of students who like each sweet mentioned .

Learn More: dress in traditional clothes

Ask the students to come dressed in their traditional clothes and speak a few sentences in their mother tongue.

Activities

Make delicious coconut *laddoos*

Materials required: Condensed milk and desiccated coconut.

How to start: In a big bowl mix together condensed milk and the coconut. You can get students to help stir the mixture in turns. Now give each child about half a tablespoonful of the mixture in the palm of their hands and show them how to roll a laddoo.

Enjoy the traditional Indian sweet with the students!

Make sure the children wash their hands before starting this activity.

Additional activities

- ➢ Ask the students to dress up in their regional dresses and come to school.
- ➢ Ask them to bring one savoury and one sweet treat native to their home state. Ask them to exchange this with their partner. This will give the students a chance to sample food typical to other states.

Answers

1. Fill in the blanks with the correct words from the brackets.

a. In the northern parts of India, ____________is preferred over rice. (**wheat**/pulses/fruits)

b. The ____________is one of the most common pieces of clothing worn by Indian women. (**saree**/jeans/pyjamas)

c. ____________grows best in regions with high rainfall. (**rice**/wheat/fruits)

d. ____________grows in areas with low rainfall. (**bajra**/ sugar cane/rice)

e. People living in Leh and Ladakh wear ____________clothes for most parts of the year. (cotton/**woollen**/nylon)

2. Write T for true and F for false.

a. We wear cotton clothes to keep us warm in winter. False

b. In the northern part of India, bajra is the staple food. False

c. Leh and Ladakh experience warm weather throughout the year. False

d. Gandhiji urged Indians to wear khadi garments. True

e. Nylon clothes do not get wet easily. True

3. Answer the following questions.

a. What is staple food?
The food that people eat in a particular region is known as the staple food of that region.

b. Name five items of clothing that are worn by women in India.
Saree, Salwar Kameez, Kurta churidar, chaniya, chaoli, odhni, pheran.

c. What are spices? Name any five.
Pepper, cardamom, cinnamon, turmeric, cloves.

d. What type of clothes do people wear in the hilly areas in winter?
People in cold regions wear woollen clothes such as shawls, scarves and sweaters, to keep their bodies warm.

e. Is eating spices in food good for health?
Many spices have with proven heart health benefits and can even ease pain and soreness. Spices also have antibacterial and antiviral properties, and most are high in vitamins and other minerals.
Eating spices in moderation is good for health, but we should not eat spices in large quantities.

f. Can we grow coconuts in Utter Pradesh? Support your answer with proper reasoning.
Coconuts grow in warm coaster regions. UP is away from the coast. It is not possible to grow coconut in UP.

4. Critical Thinking:

a. Why do people in different parts of India eat different kinds of food?
People in different parts of India eat different kinds of food. The climate and the soil of any particular region influence the types of crops that can be grown there.
For example, rice grows best in regions where there is ample rain. Rice will not grow well in Rajasthan where there is very little rainfall and the soil is very sandy. On the other hand this

type of soil is very good for growing wheat, bajra and jowar. In the western and central parts of India, wheat, bajra and jowar are widely used.

In the northern parts of the country, wheat is preferred over rice. Rice is the staple food of people living in the eastern and southern parts of India. In the coastal regions of India, fish is widely eaten.

b. People in the states of the south wear light cotton clothes. Why?

People in the states of the south wear light cotton clothes. In southern states, such as Andhra Pradesh, Telangana and Tamil Nadu the climate is warm for most parts of the year. People in these warmer states of the south wear lighter cotton clothes.

5. Social Emotional Skills:

Should we make fun of or show disgust at someone else's food? Discuss

Following points should be discussed in detail, students should give reasons.

Food is a part of local culture, traditions and habits.

We should not make fun or show disgust on food eaten by others.

6. Creativity:

Collect pictures of various types of food eaten in different states of India and make a collage in a group.

Lesson 7 Indian Culture and Traditions

Before you begin

Divide the class into five or six groups. Ask each group to find out all they can about some of the popular festivals celebrated in India. Ask them to make a small presentation in class.

They can do so by making a collage of pictures of the festival, presenting the objects associated with the festival (like a small Christmas trees for a presentation on Christmas, etc.) or by singing songs associated with a particular festival (like Christmas carols for Christmas).

As part of the second section, discuss the folk and classical dance forms of India and classical music.

Objectives

This chapter discusses in detail the various festivals that are celebrated in India. The underlying theme of the chapter is that all religions ultimately preach the same message of peace and tolerance. The chapter also covers the traditional music and dance forms of India. This chapter will provide the students with a keener understanding of:

- the festivals celebrated in India—Holi, Basant Panchami, Raksha Bandhan, Dussehra, Durga Puja, Diwali, Gurupurab, Eid-ul-Fitr, Good Friday, Christmas, Buddha Purnima and Mahavir Jayanti.
- the classical and folk dance forms of India.
- classical music—Hindustani and Carnatic music.

Explore: favourite Indian festival
Students have to tell about their favourite festival .

Learn More: Find out about Prabhat Pheris
Students have found out Prabhat Pheris.
Learn More: Find information about festivals Students have find information about Pongal, Onam, Basant Panchami and Gudi Parwa. They can consult internet, encyclopedias or their family members for this.

Explore: Watch video clips of traditional dances
Ask the students to observe the costumes and mannerisms

Learn More: Find out information about western dances
Ask the students to prepare a chart on their findings on western dances mentioned.

Learn More: learn a folk song
Students have to learn a folk song and sing it in class.

Additional activities

➢ Invite the students in your class who are training in Indian classical music or dance to put up a short performance in class. Also, ask them to talk briefly about the art form they are training in.
➢ Ask them to write a short essay about their favourite festival. Ask them to explain why they like that particular festival.

Answers

1. **The names of some Indian dances and musical instruments have been given in jumbled form below.**

Unscramble the words.

a. SSODII ______________________ Odissi
b. RWCHEA ______________________ Cheraw
c. NAOOSTR ______________________ Santoor
d. IIDUPCUHK ______________________ Kuchipudi
e. LABAT ______________________ Tabla
f. RATIS ______________________ Sitar

2. Write T for true and F for false.

a. The harvest festival of Tamil Nadu is called Onam. False (Kerala)
b. The dance form of Kuchipudi is native to Odisha. False (AP)
c. Navroz is celebrated on 25 December every year. False (21 March)
d. Cheraw is a folk dance of Mizoram. False
e. Eid-ul-Fitr is celebrated in the month of Ramadan. False

3. Answer the following questions.

a. Write ten sentences about a festival you celebrate. Students will have to provide the answers.

b. Name the holy book of the Sikhs. What is the Akhand Path?
Guru Granth Sahib is the holy book of the Sikhs.
For the three days leading up to Gurupurab, the Guru Granth Sahib is read continuously in gurudwaras. This is known as the Akhand Path. An Akjand path is followed by a langar on the last day.

c. How are folk dances different from traditional dances? In traditional dances, the dancers train with gurus or teachers for several years.
In folk dances, the dancers do not necessarily have to be trained

d. When is Eid-ul-Fitr celebrated?
Eid-ul-Fitr is celebrated by Muslims on the first day of Shawwal, marking the end of the holy month of Ramadan.

e. What would our lives be like if there were no festivals in India?
To discuss the following
Festivals are a time for celebration. They are an integral part of our rich heritage and are celebrated for different reasons. They are celebrated to welcome the seasons of the year, to mark the

different phases of the moon, to welcome the new year or to mark the birthdays of saints, gurus or leaders.

People meet relatives and friends, share gifts. People enjoy festive meals and foods.

People sing and dance on many festivals with friends, family and neighbours to share joy.

Without festivals, life would be boring and monotonous.

f. Do you think we should take certain safety measures while celebrating festivals?

We should take safety measure while celebrating festivals. Following can be discussed:

- fire hazard during Diwali
- dangerous colours and chemicals during Holi
- keep distance from the burning effigies during Dussehra
  Students should speak about local festivals and discuss dangers associated with their celebration.

4. Critical Thinking:

a. Why do we celebrate different festivals?.

- India is a land of diverse cultures and traditions.
- Festivals are an integral part of our rich heritage and are celebrated for different reasons.
- Festivals are celebrated to welcome the seasons of the year, to mark the different phases of the moon, to welcome the new year or to mark the birthdays of saints, gurus or leaders.

b. Why is India called the land of festivals?

In addition to points from above, discuss the following points

- India has many states and people following different religions stay in India.
- Many people follow different culture and traditions and each culture has festivals associated with it.
- In India, so many festivals are celebrated that not a single month goes by without a festival.

5. Social Emotional Learning:

Not everyone can afford new clothes and sweets to celebrate festivals. How can you help them? Discuss.

Students should provide answers. Discuss "joy of giving" as a concept.

6. **Creativity:**
Make Diwali cards for your friends.

Lesson 8 National Symbols and Emblem

Before you begin

Ask the students about the things give them a sense of belonging to their school. It could be the school uniform, school badge that they wear, or the school anthem that they sing. Explain to them that there are certain symbols that we regard as symbolising our Indian identity.

Objectives

This chapter educates the students about:

- the national flag.
- the national emblem.
- the national anthem.
- the meaning of Satyameva Jayate.
- the national animal, national bird, national flower, national tree, national game and the national song.

Explore: Discuss symbol/logo of school
Students have to know about the school Logo .

Circle Time: Project Tiger
Before the activity ask students to collect information about Project Tiger and Tiger sanctuaries.

Learn More: National Flower
Lotus is the national flower of Vietnam.

Explore: Learn the National Anthem
Students have to sing National Anthem in class.

Learn More: National Sport of India
Field Hockey is India's national sport. Discuss about Field Hockey in class.

Additional activities

➢ With the help of the music teacher, teach the class to sing the national anthem correctly. Make sure they pronounce the words correctly.

Explain to them the importance of standing in attention when the national anthem is being sung.

- Ask them to look up an encyclopedia and find information about the national anthem, the national flag and the national symbols.
- Help the students make an etching of the national emblem. Ask them to place a piece of white paper over the 'head' side of a Re 1 coin and rub a pencil over it. They will get a neat etch of the emblem. Ask them to cut around the circle and paste their etching in their notebooks.

Answers

1. Fill in the blanks to complete the sentences.

a. Our national flag has a ____________ in the middle, which is ____________ in colour.
Dharma Chakra, blue

b. The national emblem is adapted from ____________.
Sarnath Lion Capital

c. The national animal of India is ____________.
Bengal Tiger

d. Jana Gana Mana was written by .
Rabindranath Tagore

2. Match the following.

a. national anthem	iii. Jana Gana Mana
b. national song	iv. Vande Mataram
c. national bird	i. peacock
d. national flower	v. lotus
e. national animal	ii. tiger

3. Answer the following questions.

a. What is the Dharma Chakra?
There is a navy blue wheel or Dharma Chakra in the middle of Indian Flag in the white band. It is called the Dharma Chakra. The Dharma Chakra, also known as the Ashoka Chakra, depicts the wheel of law. It has been adapted from the Sarnath Lion Capital, which was built in the third century BCE during the reign of the Mauryan emperor, Ashoka.

b. Describe the Indian national flag.

- The national flag is the symbol of the freedom and unity of our country.

- Our national flag is rectangular in shape and consists of three colours. It is, therefore, referred to as the tricolour or the tiranga.
- It has a deep saffron (kesaria) band at the top, a white band in the middle and a green band at the bottom. Saffron stands for strength and courage.
- The white stands for peace, and the green stands for growth and prosperity.
- There is a navy blue wheel or Dharma Chakra in the middle of the white band.
- The Chakra has twenty-four spokes representing the twenty four hours in a day. It symbolises constant effort and growth.

c. What is the meaning of Satyameva Jayate? Satyameva Jayate means 'Truth Alone Triumphs'.

d. When do we sing our national anthem?
The national anthem is played or sung on national holidays, public functions and at international events.

e. Our national symbols make us feel united and proud. Explain.
These symbols are essential to the Indian identity and heritage. They remind us of India's history, diversity, natural resources and traditions. Indians of all backgrounds across the world are proud of these National Symbols as they infuse a sense of pride and patriotism in every Indian's heart.

f. We have different cultures and traditions in our country, but we are one nation. Discuss.
With 29 states and 7 union territories, India is a diverse country. It is inhabited by people who believe in many religions, follow varied tradition, culture and have multiple belief and lifestyle. Many people from each region work in other regions. Indians come together to celebrate festivals of each other. While Ganesh Chaturthi is celebrated with a lot of vigour in West India, Diwali, Holi and Janamashtami are the attractions for North, Navratra is Gujarat's. Festivals like onam, bihu, rath yatra, Pongal are now celebrated in all parts of the country.
Foods from north and east are popular in west and south and vice-a-versa.
Hindi and English as languages are used as a communication tool in many parts of India.

We unite for sports like cricket and hockey. We enjoy music, dances and movies from one part of the country across the country. India has the oldest civilization and culture and some of which is still being practiced today.

Though there is a lot of diversity and many cultures in India, it is still a living example of the famous Slogan 'Unity in Diversity'.

4. Critical Thinking:

a. Why do we have national symbols?

India is made up of a number of different state, each having its individual cultural identity. We follow different religions and customs.

National symbols are symbols which represent our country. Our national symbols give us our national identity.

b. Why is the national flag called the tricolour or tiranga?

Our national flag is rectangular in shape and consists of three colours. It is, therefore, referred to as the tricolour or the tiranga.

5. Social Emotional Skills:

We must always stand when the national anthem is being played. Do you agree with this and why?

Yes I stand up for national anthem in theaters, because I feel proud, and I think everyone should stand up too.

6. Creativity:

Find out and list the places/things where we see use the national emblem. Draw/paste pictures.

Lesson 9 Important Cities of India

Before you begin

Ask if any of the students have visited Delhi. If so, ask the student(s) to describe their experience in brief. You could also tell the students briefly about the city and its landmarks.

Display a big map of Mumbai and discuss the importance of Mumbai with the class. Tell them how it is the commercial capital of our country. Ask them to get clips from old newspapers and magazines that are relevant to Mumbai to class.

On a political map of India, point out the location of Kolkata. Ask the class if anyone has ever been to the city of Kolkata. If yes, encourage them to talk about their experience in Kolkata. Ask the class to mention all that Kolkata is famous for and list the names of famous people who are associated with Kolkata (for example, Rabindranath Tagore, Satyajit Ray, Mahashweta Devi, Raja Ram Mohan Roy, Mother Teresa, Subhash Chandra Bose, Sourav Ganguly, etc.)

Ask the class if anyone has been to Chennai. Ask them to briefly describe Chennai and their experience of the city. Show the students the exact location of Chennai on a political map of India. Explain to them how its position on the Coromandel Coast made it an ideal port for traders and merchants in the past and how it continues to be an important maritime centre.

Objectives

This chapter will help acquaint the students do Delhi, Mumbai, Kolkata and Chennai.

The chapter provides information about

- History
- its location
- its climate
- the main industries that thrive in and around the city
- important landmarks in the city

Explore: locate cities on the map

Students should be able to locate Delhi, Mumbai, Kolkata and Chennai on a map of India.

Learn More: Collect information about Delhi Metro

The class can be divided into pairs and assigned the topic

Explore: Find two interesting things about Mumbai

The class can be divided into pairs and assigned the topic

Learn More: Festivals celebrated in Mumbai

The class can be divided into pairs and assigned the topic

Explore: Eden Gardens

Eden Gardens is a cricket ground in Kolkata, India established in 1864.The stadium currently has a capacity of 68,000. The stadium is currently the largest cricket stadium in India by capacity.

Learn More: Find out main festivals celebrated in Kolkata

Durga Puja and Kali Puja

Explore: Kollywood

The Tamil-language film industry, based at Kodambakkam in S India

Learn More: Classical Singers and Bharatnatyam dancers

The class can be divided into pairs and assigned the topic

Answers

1. Draw lines to match the following.

a. film industry • • Bollywood
b. sandesh • • sweet
c. Bharatnatyam • • classical dance
d. Marina • • beach

2. Write T for true and F for false.

a. The people of Chennai speak only in Hindi. False
b. Mumbai is the commercial capital of India. True
c. The climate of Delhi is moderate. False
d. The staple diet of Bengalis is rice and fish. True
e. The Gateway of India is in Chennai. False

3. Answer the following questions.

a. What is NCR?

The National Capital Region (NCR) of Delhi is an area comprising Old Delhi, New Delhi and a few towns spread over neighbouring states such as Rajasthan, Haryana and Uttar Pradesh. The prominent cities of NCR include Delhi, Ghaziabad, Faridabad, Gurugram, Noida and Meerut.

b. How is the climate of Delhi different from that of Mumbai?

Delhi experiences extreme climatic conditions. During the summer months, it is very hot.	Since Mumbai is located next to the sea, it has warm, humid summers.
Winters are very cold.	Winters are moderate and pleasant.

The summers stretch from April to October. Hot winds known as loo blow during the peak of summer, sometimes accompanied by dust storms as well.	Between March and October, humidity is very high and the temperature ranges between 30°C and 35°C.
Monsoon is moderate while winters are very cold.	During the monsoons, it receives heavy rainfall.

c. List four tourist attractions of Kolkata. Any four below:
Fort William
- The Victoria Memorial (currently a museum famous for its statues and paintings)
- The Botanical Garden (known for its ancient banyan tree)
- The Indian Museum
- Alipore Zoo
- Birla Planetarium
- Ramakrishna Mission at Belur Math
- Eden Gardens
- The National Library (the biggest library in India)
- St. Paul's Cathedral

d. Name the important industries in Chennai. Automobile, technology, hardware manufacturing and healthcare industries.

e. Indira Gandhi Airport in Delhi is the busiest airport in India. Explain.
Reasons for Indira Gandhi Airport to be the busiest airport. Delhi is the capital of India and seat of government.
Delhi and it neighbourhood has large number of industries and companies.
Delhi is close to Agra, Jaipur and many other tourist attractions
Delhi is an educational hub

f. Seafood is very popular in cities like Kolkata and Mumbai. Discuss.
These cities are close to sea and have expanded from fishing village.
Traditionally many people staying in these areas have been fishermen.

Seafood is cheap due to proximity to sea.
Seafood has become a part of traditional diet in these areas as it was easily available and cheap.

4. **Critical Thinking:**

a. Why is rice the staple diet of Bengalis?
The weather in this area is ideal for growing rice.
Rice is growing in large quantities in these areas from olden times. Rice has become part of traditional diet due to the above reasons.

b. Why is Marine Drive is known as the Queen's Necklace?
Marine drive road is curved and has the shape of necklace. In the evening, once illuminated it appears like a necklace with shining pearls and diamonds.

5. **Social Emotional Thinking:**

How are the lives of people living in metro cities different from those of the people living in villages?
Use the following points as reference. Students can provide many other points for discussion.

Cities	**Villages**
Large population and area	Small population and small in area
Most people are engaged in jobs and business	Most people are engaged in agriculture or traditional crafts.
People user modern means of transportation like metro, taxis.	
Have pucca roads.	People use traditional means of transportation like bullock carts, tongas, etc.
Mostly have kucha roads.	
People have access to all levels of education.	Only provide access of primary and secondary education
People have access to modern hospitals and speciality clinics	Village only have a few doctors and primary health clinic with limited facilities.

6. **Creativity:**

Make a project on the city of Bengaluru. Find out details about the city's history, its climate, the important industries, its major landmarks and its culture and cuisine.

You can make your project in the form of a booklet, a chart or a computer display.

PART II: SCIENCE

Lesson 10 Living and Non-living Things

Before you begin

Take the class for a walk in the school's park or playground and ask them to observe all the things around them. Once back in class, ask them to list the things that they saw and then mark those things as living or non-living. Ask them the reasons why they think a particular object is living or non-living. List the appropriate reasons on the class board.

Objectives

The main objective of the chapter is to help the students distinguish living from non-living things by observing the following points:

- living things are able to move.
- living things breathe.
- living things need food.
- living things react to changes in their environment.
- living things reproduce.

Explore (L for Living, NL for Non-Living)

a. The boy was playing with the dog. L- Boy, dog

b. Paper can be made from plants and trees. L – Plants, Trees NL - Paper

c. Wood is used to make pencils. NL - Wood

d. Four people can play a game of carrom. L – People NL - Carrom

e. The cat sat on a tuft of grass under a tree. L – cat, grass, tree

Learn More: living and non-living

Non- living things in class – Fan, Switch, bulb, black board, desk, chair, duster, chalk, pencil, school bags, water bottles. Ask students to identify more

Activities

Help the students observe the difference between living and non-living things by conducting this very simple experiment in class.

Take two glass jars with soil in them. Put a bean seed in Jar 1 and an eraser in Jar 2. Water both jars daily. Ask the children to record the changes after a week.

They will observe that the bean seed in Jar 1 has sprouted into a small plant. But the eraser in Jar 2 remains as it was. Point out to the class that a seed is a living thing that grows while an eraser is a non-living thing and does not grow.

Additional activities

- Ask the students to list the differences and similarities between a car and a human body.
- Encourage the class to make a 'timeline'. They will need to bring their pictures; from birth to the most recent ones.

Answers

1. Classify the things in the box below into living, man-made and natural non-living things.

Living	Natural Non Living	Man made
Sparrow, tomato, plant, kangaroo, frog,	Rocks, air, river, sun	Pants, paper, factory, pen, chair

2. Write T for true and F for false. Correct the false statements.

a. Plants move from one place to another in search of food and shelter. False

b. Non-living things are either produced by humans or are naturally present. True

c. Food gives us energy to move and work. True

d. Living things do not react to changes in their environment. False

e. The Sun, the Moon and the stars are natural non-living things. True

3. Answer the following questions.

a. List three differences between living and non-living things.

Living Things	Non Living Things
Can move	Cannot move
Can breathe	Cannot breathe
Need food water and sunlight	Do not need food water and sunlight

Can grow	Cannot grow
Can remove waste.	Cannot remove waste.
Can react to changes in environment	Cannot react to changes in environment
Can reproduce	Cannot reproduce

b. Dcfinc habitat. Give examples.
The natural environment of a living thing is known as its habitat. Some habitats are large, such as forests, seas and oceans. Others are quite small, such as our own backyard or the neighbourhood park.
Examples:
Forests, Desert, Water, Marshy land, Cold region

c. Name some breathing organs of living things.
Animals use lungs
Fish use gills
Plants use pores

d. Arnav made the following observations about a plant and a worm. Which of these are correct?
(iii) A worm can go anywhere but the plant cannot is correct

e. Rina touched the leaves of a mimosa plant and they closed. This shows
(ii) It responds to stimuli. is correct

f. What would happen if all living things stopped reproducing?
Life would become extinct as no new life will be born. Students can discuss various scenarios in detail in class.

4. Critical Thinking:

a. Why do human beings need food?
Human beings need food to survive. Food provides them with the energy to perform various activities and is required for their growth and development.

b. Why do animals move from one place to another.
Animals move from one place to another for following reasons:

- In search of food and water.
- To go to a better climate – For eg. Siberian cranes come to India in winters when climate is very cold in Siberia
- To breed – For eg. in breeding season, many fish move from

rivers to sea to breed
- To be safe from predators.

5. **Social Emotional Learning:**
   Do non-living things also need care?
   Students can discuss. Use following pointers
   Take care of your notebooks – they should be clean and tidy.
   Take care of your room- keep your house clean.
   Keep your cupboard and shelves organized. Take care of your clothes.
   Take care of your bicycle, scooter, car. – They need regular service.
   Take care of all electrical appliances.
   Take care of earth – reduce pollution or air, water.

6. **Creativity:**
   Living things reproduce and have young ones. Collect pictures of animals and their offspring from magazines or the Internet. Create a chart and display it in class.

Lesson 11 Parts of a Plant

Before you begin

Bring a potted plant to class and ask the students to name the different parts of the plant as you point to them. Carefully remove the plant from the soil and have the students observe the roots. You can also show the students different plants and ask them to observe the differences between the structure of the flowers, leaves and stems.

For the second part of the chapter, bring seeds of different plants to class. Ask the students to guess the names of the plants the seeds belong to and also indicate whether they are edible or inedible. Pass the seeds around the class so that the children can observe the differences in the structure of different seeds.

Objectives

This chapter introduces the child to the different parts of a plant. In this chapter, the students will learn that:

- a plant can be divided into two main parts: the root and the shoot.

- there are two types of root systems: the tap root system and the fibrous root system.
- the function of the root is to anchor the plant to the soil and provide the plant with water and minerals.
- the stem transports nutrients to the leaves and the food produced by the leaves to all parts of the plant.
- leaves help the plant in respiration and in the production of food.
- function of flowers.
- fruits contain seeds from which new plants can germinate.
- some seeds are edible.

Explore:

Take students for a nature walk and ask them to observe parts of a plant. They should list down the parts observed in the Student book.

Name two edible and two inedible seeds.

Edible rice, corn, mustard

Non edible - apple, orange, mango, papaya Accept other appropriate answers

Circle Time

Discuss importance of plants and ways to conserve them. Ask students to share their views.

Learn More

Fruit – coconut, cucumber, tomato Leaf – spinach, cabbage

root – carrot Seed - rajma

Activities

What happens when a leaf is kept away from sunlight? Conduct the following experiment in class to help the children understand the role of sunlight in the process of photosynthesis.

Materials required: Brown paper envelope, sticky tape and a potted plant.

Method: Cover one leaf of the green potted plant complctely with the brown paper envelope. Secure the envelope with sticky tape. Place this plant in a sunny spot in the classroom. Remove the envelope after five days. Observe how the leaf looks in comparison to the other leaves.

Write down your observation. The students will observe that the leaf that was covered has become pale and lost its green colour.

Additional activities

- Encourage the class to grow a potato; using the eyes of the potato.
- Did you know that some plants grow/survive in water? They do not require soil. Encourage the class to find out, what is 'Hydroponics'?

Answers

1. Complete the crossword.

ACROSS

1	Plants make their food through this process	Photosynthesis
3	It bears leaves, flowers and fruits	Stem
7	Plants need this gas for photosynthesis	Carbon di oxide
8	The part where most plants make their food	Leaves

DOWN

1	Unscramble NLPAT	Plant
2	It germinates to form a plant	Seed
4	Plants produce and release this gas	Oxygen
5	Source of energy and warmth	Sun
6	Used by many plants to absorb water and minerals from the soil	roots
9	Food is stored in the different parts of a plants in the form of	starch

2. Write O for the fruits that have one seed and M for the fruits that have many seeds.

O	M
Mango, Peach	Orange, Papaya, Apple, Watermelon,

3. Answer the following questions.

a. Define photosynthesis.

Plants manufacture food using carbon dioxide and water, in the presence of sunlight and a green-coloured pigment called chlorophyll, which is found in all green plants.

This process of making food by green plants is known as photosynthesis.

b. Give four examples of leaves that we eat. Spinach, coriander, lettuce, fenugreek, mint, basil

c. What is chlorophyll?
   Chlorophyll is a green-coloured pigment which is found in all green plants. It helps in the process of making food(photosynthesis) by using sunlight and water.

d. Which of the following is not a root?
   (ii) potato

e. Grapevines are an example of a climber. They climb because
   (i) they have weak stems and need support.

f. What would happen if there were no flowers?
   Flowers are structures responsible for producing seeds. Seeds grow into new plants. Thus, flowers help a plant reproduce. Some flowers change into fruits.

Use the following points for discussion:

- Without flowers, plants will not be able to reproduce.
- We will not get many fruits.
- Many flowers are used for making colours and scent. These will not be available.

4. Critical Thinking:

a. Why flower is an important part of a plant?
   Flowers are structures responsible for producing seeds. Seeds grow into new plants. Thus, flowers help a plant grow more of its own kind.
   Some flowers change into fruits.

b. The leaf is known as the kitchen of the plants. Why?
   Leave are called kitchen of the plants because:

- They are responsible for converting sunlight and nutrients into food.
- Plants manufacture food using carbon dioxide and water, in the presence of sunlight and a green-coloured pigment called chlorophyll, which is found in all green plants.
- This process of making food by green plants is known as photosynthesis.

5. Social Emotional Learning:

How are plants and animals dependent on each other? Discuss. You may use the following pointers

Plants need animals	Animals need plants

Plants use nutrients from soil that are provided by animals (soil microbes).	For food and nutrition.
For carrying seeds to other places.	For shelter – nest of birds.
Many small animals make homes in trees.	
Need carbon di oxide that is given by animals.	Need oxygen that is given by plants.

6. **Creativity:**
   Collect different types of pulses and leaves. Make a collage in a group.

Lesson 12 Animals

Before you begin

Ask your students to observe animals that are commonly seen in cities, towns and villages. Ask them to look up books, and bring pictures of animals to class. If possible, organize a trip to the nearest zoo to observe different animals.

Objectives

The chapter aims to familiarize students with animals.

The students will learn class animals on the basis of what they eat.

Student will learn the terms

- carnivorous
- herbivorous
- omnivorous
- frugivorous
- Food chain

Students will learn to classify animals on the basis of

- how they live
- how they look
- how they give birth to young ones.

Explore: Guess the names of animals

a) Frog
b) Monkey
c) Spider
d) Tortoise
e) Giraffe

Learn More: Fun facts about animals and share Ask student to access internet, encyclopedia and other books to find fun fact about animals.

Additional Activities

- If possible, show the students a few documentaries on animals.
- Ask students to find the names of wild life sanctuaries and national parks in India. Ask them to mark these out on a map of India.
- Make 6 groups and assign one National part to each group. Students have to find information about the park and share it with class. They have to prepare charts with this information and present it to the class.

Answers

1. Name three animals that

a. live on land — Elephant, horse, lion, tiger…
b. live in water — fish, octopus, dolphins, whales
c. can fly — sparrow, pigeon, crow, eagle, vulture
d. can swim — fish, duck, crocodile, frogs,
e. can hop — kangaroo, rabbit, frog, grasshopper

2. Classify these animals as amphibian, fish, reptile, bird or mammal.

Amphibian	Fish	Reptile	Mammal	Bird
salamander	Shark,	Snake,	Dolphin,	Parrot,
	octopus	Turtle	gorilla,	swan,
			leopard, Seal,	Peacock
			elephant, lion,	
			chimpanzee	

3. Answer the following questions.

a. What are mammals? How are they different from insects?
Mammals are warm-blooded animals. These animals can keep their body temperature higher than their surroundings. They give birth to young ones and feed their babies milk. They breathe with

the help of lungs. Most mammals have hair or fur covering their bodies.

Insects are small animals. Mammals are bigger

Most insects have six leg and can fly. Most mammals have 4 limbs and cannot fly (a few can).

Insects breathe using small holes called spiracles. Mammals breathe using lungs.

b. Differentiate between herbivores and carnivores.

Herbivores	Carnivores
Eat only plants.	Only eat flesh and other animals.
Their sharp front teeth help them tear off leaves from plants. Strong, broad teeth at the back of their mouth help them chew their food.	They have sharp, pointed and curved teeth for tearing flesh.

c. What is the food chain? Explain with the help of an example.

All green plants are called producers as they prepare food for other animals and plants.

All other living beings obtain food from plants, therefore they are called consumers.

Herbivores eat plants directly. All carnivores eat herbivores. This chain of living beings eating and being eaten is called the food chain.

For example, an insect eats food grains, a frog eats insects and a snake eats the frog.

d. Pick the odd one out

(i) elephant - others are carnivores

e. A food chain always starts with

(iii) green plants

f. What will happen if all tigers are killed? Should be discussed in the following manner:

- It leads to an imbalance.
- When the predator ceases to exist, the prey will flourish.
- This will lead to scarcity its food sources and that might lead to other species going extinct.
- Tigers as predators are necessary to keep population of certain

species in check.

4. **Critical Thinking:**

a. Why are humans called omnivores?
Humans eat animals and plant. Therefore, they are called omnivores.

b. Why are plants called producers?
Only green plants can prepare their own food by photosynthesis. Plants are called producers as they prepare food for other animals and plants.

5. **Social Emotional Learning:**
Do you use articles made from animal skins? Many animals are killed for their skin. Is it right to kill animals for commercial purposes? Discuss.
This can be discussed in class. Teacher should guide the discussion.

6. **Creativity:**
Go for a nature walk around your school or home. Find one example of the following kinds of animals. Name them, draw/paste their pictures and make a chart.
Two-legged Four-legged Six-legged Eight-legged Many-legged

Lesson 13 Birds

Before you begin

Ask your students to observe birds commonly seen in cities. You can ask them to also look up books and bring pictures of birds to class. If possible, organise a trip to the bird park to observe different varieties of birds.

Objectives

This chapter aims to familiarise the students with birds. Different parts of a bird are discussed including:

- beak.
- wings.

- claws.

This chapter also discusses nests of different birds.

Additional activities

- If possible, show the students a small documentary on birds.
- Ask them to find the names of the bird sanctuaries in India. Ask them to mark out the bird sanctuaries on a blank map of India. Ask them to find information on the birds found in these sanctuaries.

Explore: Go for nature walk

Students have to draw the beaks of the birds observed during nature walk.

Explore: Claws matched to birds

1. duck
2. sparrow
3. eagle
4. sandpiper
5. penguin

Learn More: Colour

Colour the scarlet macaw.

Answers

1. **What kinds of beaks do the following birds have? What are they used for?**

   hummingbird

   They have beaks like a straw. Their long, pointed beaks help them to drink nectar from flowers. The beak acts like a straw and helps it to reach deep into flowers and sip nectar.

   duck

   Ducks have broad and flat beaks, known as bills, with holes on either side. The beak acts as a strainer, as the muddy water flows out through the holes, leaving behind the worms and the small fish in the bird's bill.

   sparrow

   Sparrows have strong, short, thick and cone-shaped beaks. They use it for breaking open seeds.

   robin

   Robins have strong, short, thick and cone-shaped beaks. They use it for breaking open seeds.

spoonbill

Spoonbills have broad and flat beaks, known as bills, with holes on either side. The beak acts as a strainer, as the muddy water flows out through the holes, leaving behind the worms and the small fish in the bird's bill.

2. Write T for true and F for false. Correct the false statements.

a. Pigeons have hooked beaks. False

b. A woodpecker has a chisel-shaped beak. True

c. Eagles have talons. True

d. Crows have webbed feet. False

3. Answer the following questions.

a. Differentiate between flight feathers and down feathers.

Down feathers	**Flight Feathers**
They are all over the body of the bird	They are long and flat and arc found on the wings and the tail.
They help a bird to stay warm.	They help the bird to steer and fly.

b. What type of feet do ducks and geese have? How are they useful?

Ducks and geese have webbed feet that help them swim in water. The webbing helps them to paddle and push water

c. What are talons?

Eagles and vultures have very sharp claws, known as talons. These help them to catch their prey such as frogs, mice and rats.

d. Which one of the following birds does not live in water?

(i) koel

e. All of the following are parts of a birds except:

(iv) gill

f. Can you fly? How do bird's fly? No, we cannot fly.

Birds fly with the help of wings. They flap their wings upwards and downwards to fly.

Strong flight muscles help them to move their wings. They have hollow bones which make their bodies light They have streamlined bodies.

Their tails help them to change direction.

4. **Critical Thinking:**

a. Why do birds have different types of beaks?
A bird uses its beak to catch food and eat. Different birds have different kinds of beaks depending upon the type of food they eat.

b. Birds make nests. Why?
Birds make their nests only when they have to lay eggs. Nests are useful to keep their eggs protected.

5. **Social Emotional Learning:**
How is the female cuckoo bird different from other female birds? Is it right to do what is does?
Cukoo does not take care of its eggs.
The female cuckoo bird looks for a nest of another bird, which already has eggs in it. She pushes the eggs out and lays her own. When the baby cuckoo is born, the foster parents continue to work hard to feed it.
Teacher can discuss about the selfish nature of cuckoo why it is not good to be selfish.

6. **Creativity:**
Make a bird feeder with the help of a used plastic bottle.

Lesson 14 The Human Body

Before you begin

Take the students to the science lab and show them a diagram of the human body and the human skeleton. If possible, show them simple diagrams of the circulatory system, respiratory system, skeletal, muscular system, digestive system, the nervous system, the excretory and the reproductive system.

Objectives

This chapter aims to make the students aware of the basic functions of:

- the circulatory system;
- the respiratory system;
- the skeletal system;

- the muscular system;
- the digestive system;
- the nervous system;
- the excretory and reproductive systems.

Activities

Explore: Parts of body we use to do an action

- walk feet
- jump feet
- blink eyes
- wink eyes
- breathe nose
- smell nose
- chew mouth, teeth

Circle Time : Broken bones

Any student/s or the teacher can share the experience.

- How did the bone break?
- What was the treatment?
- How long was the treatment?
- What difficulties were faced in daily life?

Learn More: Joints used to do actions

looking sideways	neck
waving goodbye	wrist,
kicking a ball	hip, knee, ankle
drawing a sketch	wrist, finger
touching your toes	backbone, hip
skipping	wrist, toes

Learn More

Encourage the students to look up an encyclopedia and find out how creatures such as whales, that have lungs, can stay under water for long periods of time.

Learn More: Circle Time

Discuss with the class what is meant by indigestion and why we sometimes get a stomachache. Give them time to expand on their own ideas. Explain to them that indigestion usually occurs when we eat very spicy or fatty foods. Our stomach is not able to digest such foods easily and as a result we feel bloated, our stomach hurts and sometimes we have an upset tummy. Sometimes we get a stomachache because we have eaten food that has gone bad or was not hygienic. Germs in spoilt or unclean food can cause us to have an infection which results in a stomach ache and/or an upset tummy.

Additional activities

- Have a quiz on body parts in class. You can divide the class into teams or make this an individual competition. You can describe or define a body part and have the class guess what it is. For instance, you could ask 'I am a bony cage that protects the lungs and heart' (answer: rib cage), or 'I am a sense organ located inside your mouth' (answer: tongue)
- Make labels of different body parts (head, neck, hand, hip, etc.) and stick some adhesive tape behind the labels. Hang a big picture of the human body (which is not labelled) in class. Now call your students to come by turns and stick the labels you hand out to them in the appropriate place on the human body. You can do this same activity with the different organ systems in the body.

Answers

1. **Match the organ to its system.**

heart •	• circulatory system
lungs •	• respiratory system
skull •	• skeletal system
kidneys •	• excretory system
muscles •	• muscular system
intestines •	• digestive muscular system
brain •	• nervous system

2. **Find these body parts in the grid. You need to look across, down and diagonally.**
   Students can do this

3. **Answer the following questions.**

a. What is an organ system? List the various organ systems. Many organs performing the same function together form an organ system. There are many organ systems in our body to perform different functions.

Respiratory System

Circulatory System
Digestive System
Skeletal System
Nervous System
Excretory System
Reproductive System

b. What are nerves?

The brain has messengers known as nerves.

Brains uses nerves to send instructions to the muscles, bones and so on, telling them what to do. Nerves also carry messages from the organs to the brain.

c. Write the functions of the following organ systems.

(i) skeletal system

The skeleton forms a framework that supports the body. It provides protection, reducing risk of injury to the internal organs.

(ii) digestive system

The digestive system breaks the food eaten by the body into smaller parts that can be absorbed into the blood and carried to cells throughout the body.

(iii) circulatory system

The circulatory system carries materials throughout the entire body. It transports oxygen, water and nutrients to the cells and carries away wastes produced by the cells.

(iv) respiratory system

The respiratory system helps us breathe.

d. The organs which are like the electric wiring in our body are.

(i) nerves

e. Kailash plays cricket. Which body systems help him to run, jump and hit the ball?

(iv) both (i) and (ii)

f. How do broken bones get healed?

In the first few days after a fracture, the body forms a blood clot around the broken bone to protect it and deliver the cells needed for healing.

Then, an area of healing tissue forms around the broken bone. This is called a callus. It joins the broken bones together. It's soft at first, then gets harder and stronger over the following weeks.

4. Critical Thinking:

a. Why is the heart one of the most important organs in our body?
The heart is one of the most important organs in the body. It pumps blood throughout our body. The blood is carried by the blood vessels and contains oxygen, water and nutrients to all body parts. All body parts are able to function if there is adequate supply of blood.

b. Why should we chew our food properly?
Our body eats food that can be digested by breaking it into smaller parts. Chewing food properly breaks it into small parts. This makes it easy to digest.

5. **Social Emotional Learning:**
How does an organ system works? Have you ever worked in a team? What are the benefits of working in a team? Many organs performing the same function together form an organ system.
Benefits of working in a team:

- Working together lets team members build on the strengths of other teammates.
- A team can accomplish much more than the single members can do individually.
- In a good team, team members are able to respond to each other and change their responses as needed to function properly.
- In most cases, a team can deal with complicated problems more effectively than individuals can.

6. **Creativity:**
Tick the box appropriately

Lesson 15 Food

Before you begin

Ask students the food they eat. Ask them why we need to eat food. Encourage them to tell about food which is cooked at their respective houses. Ask them if they know the difference between healthy food and junk food. Explain as required.

Objectives

This chapter introduces children to:

- Differentiate between healthy and non-healthy food
- Balanced diet
- Staying healthy
- Foodborne illnesses

Explore: classify healthy and junk food

Healthy	Junk
Carrot, Sandwich, Soup, Egg, grilled chicken, apple, pasta, milk	Donuts, Fried chicken, pastry, seekh kabab, chips, fries, cold drink

Circle Time: Discuss favourite food Students to provide answers. Teacher to ask students to identify nutrients in the foods mentioned. Accept all appropriate answers.

Learn More: Unhealthy food choices
Ask students to refer to internet and encyclopedias to find out about problems faced on eating unhealthy/junk foods.

Additional Activities

- ➢ Students can talk about the foods from their regions and do a show and tell
- ➢ A food festival can be organized in the class where students bring one dish each which belong to their region
- ➢ Discuss why it is important to eat fresh produce

Answers

1. **Give two examples of each.**

a. protein rich foods ________________________
eggs, milk, fish

b. foods that provide us energy ____________________
wheat, rice, potatoes

c. foods that contain minerals and vitamins ______________
fruits, vegetables and nuts

2. **Fill in the blanks to complete the following statements.**

a. We must eat from all the. ____________
food groups

b. We get most of our food from ____________

and animals. plants

c. We must _______________ our hand before we eat. wash

d. We should _______________ for eight hours in a day. sleep

e. We must _______________ our food properly. chew

3. Answer the following questions.

a. What are nutrients? Give examples.

The food substances which are required by our body are called nutrients. All healthy food items have various nutrients. Proteins – found in fish, milk, eggs and eggs Carbohydrates – found in wheat, rice, potatoes Vitamins – found in fruits, vegetables and nuts Fat – found in butter, oil and ghee

b. Drinking plenty of water helps us. How?

Water helps in blood circulation, digestion and maintaining body temperature. Water also helps to flush out waste products and toxins from our body. Therefore, we should drink plenty of water every day.

c. What is a balanced diet?

Diet which has all the nutrients in the proper amounts, is called balanced diet. Eating a balanced diet means having food from all the food groups in proper proportions in our meals. A balanced diet helps us to grow properly and keeps us healthy, strong and active.

d. All the food items listed below are rich in proteins, except.

(iv) cucumber

e. Cereals are an important source of .

(iii) carbohydrates

f. What would happen if you stopped eating green vegetables?

Dark green leafy vegetables are good sources of many vitamins and minerals (such as iron and calcium). They're also great sources of fiber. This fibrous substance is called roughage. We need roughage as it helps to remove solid waste from our body. Nutrients found in dark green leafy vegetables may prevent certain types of cancers and promote heart health.

If we do not eat green vegetables, mineral balance of the body will be disturbed. The body's ability to remove solid waste from the body will also be affected. This will have a negative impact on the health.

4. Critical Thinking:

a. Cereals and pulses should be cooked before eating. Why?
Cooking of cereals and pulses:
- makes the food tasty.
- makes food easy to chew and digest.
- kills the germs present in raw food.

b. Why should we have a balanced diet?
Eating a balanced diet means having food from all the food groups in proper proportions in our meals. A balanced diet helps us to grow properly and keeps us healthy, strong and active.

5. **Social Emotional Learning:**
Why should we eat breakfast? Do you eat breakfast before going to school?
Breakfast gives us energy needed to get things done and help us focus on activities at school.
Breakfast also provides nutrients and mineral from foods like milk, cereals, eggs and vegetables.
Those are just a few reasons why we should eat breakfast.

6. **Creativity:**
Track your diet for one day.
Observe and list all the things you eat. Place them in the correct rows. Are you eating a balanced diet?

Lesson 16 The Universe and the Solar System

Before you begin

Tell the students to look at the night sky and the morning sky before starting this chapter. Ask them to talk about what they saw. Encourage them to share in class what they know about the universe and the solar system. Ask them to bring books with pictures of the universe and the solar system to class.

Objectives

This chapter introduces the students to:
- the concept of the universe.
- definition of constellation.

- a basic idea of the Big Bang Theory.
- introduction to the sun and the planets of the solar system.
- satellites.
- eclipses.
- the rotation and the revolution of the earth.

Explore: Observe night sky
Students will describe the night sky.

Explore: Big Bang
Ask students to find out information about "big bang" from internet and encyclopedia.

Explore: Colour
Students have to colour the picture of the globe as per instructions.

Learn More: Find out about Astronomers
An astronomer is a scientist who studies astronomical objects such as stars, planets, moons, comets, and galaxies.
Ask the students to find out names of 5 famous astronomers (at least 2 Indian)

Additional activities

- ➢ Involve the whole class in making a model of the solar system. Ask the students to use their creativity. They can use balls (table tennis balls, tennis balls or rubber balls for the smaller planets, footballs or basketballs for the giant planets). These balls can be covered in paper and then coloured in order to look like the planets. For instance, since Venus is the brightest planet, it can be covered in bright glitter, Mars can be painted red, Saturn should be given rings around it, etc.
  The students could also choose to make a much smaller model of the solar system. They could make it on chart paper. The planets can be made of bits of thermocoal and their orbits can be marked with glitter.
- ➢ Organise a quiz in class on this chapter. You can divide the class into teams or make this an individual competition. Questions could include 'list the planets in order of their distance from the sun', 'name the four rock planets', 'a lunar eclipse occurs every month—true or false', etc.

Answers

1. **Write T for true and F for false. Correct the false statements.**

a. An orbit is the path that the Sun moves on. False

b. The lunar cycle is of 40 days. False

c. A natural satellite is a celestial body that orbits a planet. True

d. The Earth's is an imaginary line going from the North Pole to the South Pole. False

e. Planets have their own light. False

2. **Find and colour these words in the grid.**

Students can find the words in the grid

3. **Answer the following questions.**

a. What is the Solar System? Name all the planets of our Solar System.

The Solar System is made up of the Sun, which is the central star, the planets that circle it.

The eight planets are:

Mercury, Venus, Earth, Mars, Jupiter, Saturn, Uranus and Neptune

b. What causes day and night? Explain with the help of a diagram.

- The Earth rotates from the West to the East. It takes twenty-four hours to rotate once.
- The time it takes for the Earth to complete one rotation is known as one day.
- As the Earth rotates on its axis, part of the Earth faces the Sun and the other half is away from the Sun.
- The part facing the Sun has day at that time and the other half, which is away from the Sun, has night.
- As the Earth spins, we move through the light into the darkness and back again. This results in day and night.

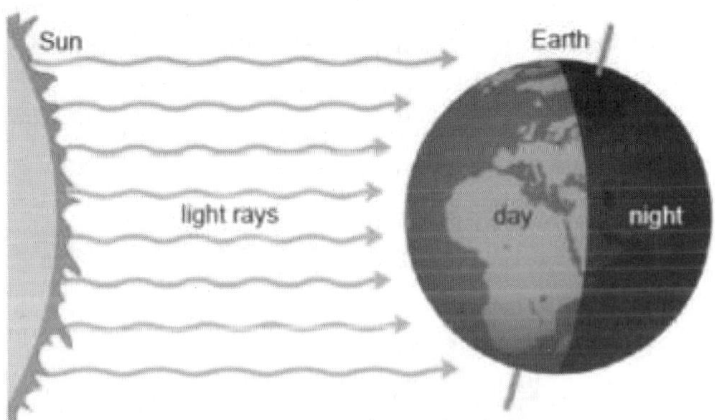

day and night on the Earth

Rotation is when a planet or its moon turns all the way around on its axis. The Earth rotates around an axis, known as its rotational axis. The Earth rotates from the West to the East.

While the Earth spins or rotates on its axis, it also simultaneously moves around the Sun on a fixed path known as its orbit. This movement of a planet around any other objects is known as revolution.

The Earth's orbit is oval or elliptical in shape. The Earth takes 365 1/4 days to complete one revolution around the Sun.

c. Differentiate between rotation and revolution of the Earth.

d. The solar system is part of the _______________.
(ii) Milky Way

e. Most planets move along me as they revolve around the Sun. I am fixed and normally elliptical. Who am I?
(ii) orbit

f. What would happen if the Earth stops rotating on its axis? If the earth stops rotating one part of earth will always be dark and the other part will always have light and sunny.

- The dark part of earth will become very cold.
- The part that is facing the sun will be very hot.
- This will affect climate, vegetation and all life. Students can discuss various scenarios.

4. Critical Thinking:

a. Why do you think the Moon shines at night?
The moon shines at night as the Sun's light that fall on moon is reflected by the Moon.

b. Life exists only on the Earth. Why?
The presence of air, water and the correct temperature makes it possible for life to exist on Earth.
We are not aware that other planets have air, water and the correct temperature for life.

5. Social Emotional Learning:

Can we see a clear sky in big cities these days?
Why is it so? Discuss.
We cannot see a clear sky in big cities.
Big cities have a large population and a large number of industries and vehicles that cause air pollutions. We cannot see clear sky because of air pollution caused by vehicles and

industries.
This can be discussed in detail in class.

6. **Creativity & Informational Literacy**
Identify the people in the following pictures. Collect information about their achievements.
Kalpana Chawla, Sunita Williams and Rakesh Sharma

Lesson 17 Natural Resources

Before you begin

Ask the students to cut out pictures from old newspapers and magazines that show how air, water, plants, rocks and minerals are useful in our everyday lives. Ask them to stick these pictures on a sheet of chart paper and make a collage. Ask them what it would be like if these resources were not available to us.

Objectives

This chapter aims to familiarise the students with some common natural resources and their uses.

The topics covered in this chapter include:

- definition of a natural resource.
- water and its uses.
- air and its uses.
- trees and plants and how they are useful to us.
- rocks and soil and their uses.

Explore: Things which are not made by humans Students to provide answers. Accept all appropriate answers. The source of all things is nature.

Explore: Collect soil and observe
Students will describe what they see in the soil. Accept all appropriate answers.

Learn More: Experiment
The heaviest components of the soil will settle at the bottom. Water will be clean at the top. Help students identify the type of soil.

Explore: Colour things made of metal

Students colour: scissors, gate, brush, watch

Circle Time: Discuss on conservation of natural resources.

- Avoid using ACs and heaters too much.
- Water plants with a watering can instead of a water pipe or sprinkler. More water feeds the plant and less water is used overall.
- Reuse and Recycle wherever possible.
- Water the lawn during the cooler parts of the day to avoid loss of water from evaporation and wind.
- Grow a little garden of herbs, vegetables, and fruits.
- Avoid using petrol/diesel vehicle for small journeys.
- Car/bus Engine should be stopped at traffic lights. Student should provide other answers.

Additional activities

➢ Grow a class garden. Get the whole class involved in this activity. Divide the class into groups and make each group responsible for procuring one item for your class garden. To make the garden, get a medium-sized glass aquarium. Ask one group to fill the bottom with rocks. The next group has to layer some gravel on top of the rocks. The third group will now need to place sand above the gravel, while the fourth group will place a humus-clay mix as the topmost layer. Ask the fifth group to collect some grass (with soil still attached to the roots) and plant it above the layer of humus and clay. The last group has to collect some earthworms and place them in the garden. Water this garden regularly and place it where it can get some sun. Soon this class garden will be blooming. The students will also be able to see the layers of the soil and how earthworms burrow in and out of the soil.

Answers

1. **Name five things that live in the soil and draw any two.**
   earthworms, ants, termites, beetles, rats,

2. **Fill in the blanks with the correct words from the brackets.**

a. ___Metal___ is a natural resource.
(plastic/metal/building)

b. Oxygen gas is released during photosynthesis.
(Oxygen/Carbon dioxide/Nitrogen)

c. Rubies are used in jewellery.
(rubies/soil/plants)

d. Soil is the topmost layer of the Earth's crust.
(coal/soil/mineral)

e. Different rocks make different soils.
(rocks/gases/plants)

3. Answer the following questions.

a. What are natural resources? Name any four.
Natural resources are substances which are not man-made. These are found in or on the Earth's crust and in oceans, forests and mountains.
Oil, coal, natural gas, metals and minerals are all examples of natural resources.

b. What is soil? How is it formed?
Soil is the topmost layer of the Earth's crust.
Soil is formed by the breaking of rocks into small pieces over a long period of time.

- Plants obtain minerals from the soil. Soil is made up of mineral particles, water, air and living organisms as well as non-living material. Soil contains gravel, sand, clay and humus.
- The topmost layer has dead leaves, twigs and decomposed parts of dead animals, which make it very fertile and good for growing plants.

c. What are the various sources of water? Sources of water are:
Oceans, seas, rivers, lakes and ponds, underground water and glaciers.

d. Pick the odd one out.
(iv) diamond

e. Which of these is not one of the main components of the air all around us?
(iv) Sulphur dioxide

f. Is soil living or non-living?
Soil is made up of minerals, air, water and organic matter in form of living plants and small animals.
In itself, soil is not a living thing, but is an environment full of life. The healthier the soil, more it is able to support life.

4. **Critical Thinking:**

a. Humus is important for plant growth.
Humus is the top most layer of soil that has dead leaves, twigs and decomposed parts of dead animals that make it very fertile and good for growing plants.

b. Why do we need air?
Air is made up of different gases, mainly nitrogen, oxygen and carbon dioxide along with water vapour.

Use the following points for discussion in class

a. Oxygen in the air is necessary for respiration and combustion, while
b. Carbon dioxide is used by green plants to prepare food.
c. Air is used as a medium to transmit sound. We will not be able to hear each other if there is no air.
d. Air is used for transportation as a sail in a boat or a ship
e. Air is required to maintain temperature.
f. Air is useful for water cycle – evaporation, condensation, rainfall.

5. **Social Emotional Learning:**

Discuss ways to keep the air clean.
Discussion pointers:
Walk, bike, carpool, or use public transport.
Use CNG in place of diesel/petrol.
Reduce usage of electricity – switch off when not in use.
Say no to burning of leaves.
Know before you go. If you need to drive, plan the most fuel efficient route Avoiding areas of high traffic. When you must drive, combine trips and car pool.
Turn off your car's engine while waiting for someone or at traffic light.
Use limited pesticides.
Check your tyre pressure. Properly inflated tires improve fuel efficiency.
Students can provide more answers.

6. **Creativity:**

Make a list of metals used at your home. Which is the most expensive metal? Why is it so expensive? Find out.

Lesson 18 Matter and Its Properties

Before you begin

Get many different kinds of objects to the class like a block of wood, a metal ruler or block, modelling clay, soap bubbles, cotton balls, jelly, an inflated balloon, a football, a block of ice, a jug of water, thick glue, etc. Let the class feel these things and observe them carefully. Now ask them to list these things as solids, liquids and gases. Explain to them that although jelly, modelling clay or a ball of cotton can be squeezed, they still have a definite shape and are, therefore, solids. Solids can be hard or soft but have a definite size and shape.

Now, pour some water from a jug first into a long narrow vase and then into a flat dish. Ask the students to observe how water (or any liquid) takes on the shape of its container.

Now take an inflated balloon and squeeze it into different shapes. Ask the students what happens to the air inside. Ask them to observe how the air takes the shape of its container too.

Objectives

This chapter deals with matter and its properties. The topics covered in this chapter are:

- properties of objects—all objects take up space and have mass. Objects that take up space and have mass are called matter.
- matter can exist in three states—solid, liquid or gas.
- discussion of the properties of solids.
- discussion of the properties of liquids.
- discussion of the properties of gases.
- changes in states of matter.

Explore: Experiment

No, the book does not spread on the floor like water.

Explore: Observation

Water vapour is a gas and it does not have a shape.

Circle Time: Weave a story

Student should use imagination and make a story about water cycle.

Activities

Ask the students to observe what happens when water is boiled and water vapour is formed.

Take the class to the science lab. Ask them to observe carefully what happens as water starts boiling in a beaker. Ask them to notice how water changes into steam (water vapour) and escapes from the beaker.

Additional Activities

- Ask the students to make a list of all the solids, liquids and gases that they see at home or are used in their homes.
- Bring some common items and ask the students to classify them as solids, liquids or gases.

Answers

1. In each box, write S for solid, L for liquid and G for gas.

petrol	lemonade,	L
wind	our breath	G
ice cream flower		S

2. Write T for true and F for false. Correct the false statements.

a. Anything that has mass is matter. True

b. Air occupies space. True

c. Water has no definite shape, therefore, it is not matter. False

d. You cannot change the shape of a solid. False

e. Air will expand to fill the space it is kept in. True

3. Answer the following questions.

a. What is matter? Name the three states of matter.

Anything that occupies space and has mass is called matter. Everything around us is made up of matter.

Matter exists in three different states: solid, liquid and gas.

b. Write three properties of gases.

A gas has the following properties:

- no definite shape
- no definite volume
- occupies all the space available

c. Name five liquids that are used in our homes. What are they used for?

Milk, Water – drinking

Oil - cooking

Cleaning Liquid, Shampoo, - cleaning
Kerosene, Diesel– As a fuel

d. Which of the following is an example of matter?
(iv) all of these

e. Which of the following will flow?
(iii) milk (iv) oxygen

f. What is your physical state? Are you solid, liquid or gas? The human body is made out of lots of different states, so a human body is not just one state of matter, but is rather made from many different states of matter. 60% of an adult's body is made of water, which means that the human body would be at least 60% liquid.

4. Critical Thinking:

a. A block of wood is solid. Why is it so?
A block of wood is solid because it has a fixed shape and size.

b. When our mother is cooking food in the kitchen, we can smell the food in the other room as well. Why?
The smell of food gets mixed with air and then moves with air from the kitchen to the other rooms.

5. Social Emotional Learning:

List any five liquids which you should not drink. Petrol
Kerosene Pesticides Cleaning liquids Shampoo

6. Creativity:

Observe the activities done in your kitchen. Write two examples of the following changes.

Lesson 19 Energy and Forces

Before you begin

Before you start this lesson, ask the students to list the different forms of energy they see around them. Gradually steer them towards the understanding that energy is the ability to do work. Help them see that light, sound, heat, electricity etc., are different forms of energy.

As part of the second part of the chapter, help observe that things move or change direction when they are pushed or pulled. Explain to the class that push or pull is referred to as force. Introduce them to the concepts of gravity and friction by asking them to observe these phenomena in their daily lives.

Give them some examples that they can grasp easily (things thrown up in the air always come down, it is very hard to pull an object along a rough surface, etc.)

Objectives

This chapter seeks to familiarise the students with energy and forces. The topics covered in this chapter include:

- light—sources and uses.
- sound.
- force.
- different types of forces—gravity and friction.

Explore: Tick the appropriate box Pushed- Baby pram, Tree, bottle, Dustbin Pulled- Golf set, Girl pulling a chicken

Explore: Discuss energy provided by food
Can you do work without eating food? For how long can you live without eating food? Discuss.
We can only survive for a few days without eating food.

- The body will not get nourishment.
- The organs will not be able to perform their functions.
- The body will feel weak.

Explore: discuss how light travels
We cannot see light through a bent pipe.

Explore: sound vibrations
Yes we can hear vibrations when a guitar string is plucked.

Additional activities

➢ Conduct this simple experiment to show the class that sound is actually vibrations that travel through air.
What you need: 1 rubber band, 1 piece of plastic, 1 large can, 1 wood ruler, 1 small can and some salt.
What to do: Pull the plastic tightly over the open end of the large can and hold it down tightly and put the rubber band over it. Sprinkle some salt on top of the plastic. Hold the small can close to the salt and tap the side of the small can with the ruler. Ask the students to take turns or to come up in small groups to observe what happens to the salt.

They will see the salt bouncing up and down even though it is not being touched. It does so because the plastic is vibrating. The plastic is vibrating because of the sound waves hitting it. Sound is actually vibrations that travel through the air.

Answers

1. **Draw an arrow to show the direction in which the baby's cart will move.**
   Students can draw the direction

2. **Write T for true and F for false. Correct the false statements.**

a. Force can make a moving object change its direction. True

b. Things at rest will start moving by themselves. False

c. Force is a push or a pull. True

d. Wind and water both exert force. True

e. To generate force, we must have energy. True

3. **Answer the following questions.**

a. What is force? What are its effects?
   Force means applying a push or a pull to move any object.

- Force can change the shape of any object.
- Force can also make moving objects stop or speed up.
- It can change the direction of movement as well.

b. What is energy? Name the different forms of energy. Energy is the ability to do work.
   There are different forms of energy. Chemical energy, Light, Sound and Heat are different forms of energy.

c. Name four things that make a sound in the classroom, in the school bus, at home and in the playground.
   Class room – fan, chalk writing on board, clapping by hands, shoes while walking.
   School bus – horn, the engine, the opening of door, mobile phone.
   Home Fan, cooking sounds, opening and shutting of doors/ windows, refrigerator, washing machine, mixer, telephone.
   Playground – running, whistles of referee, clapping by hands, birds.

d. Sound is produced by __________.
   (ii) vibrations

e. I squeeze, I stretch, I push, I pull, I make things move, Who am I?
(iii) force

f. What would happen if you jump in space?
You will continue to move in the direction of the jump as there is no gravitation force to pull you back or friction to stop you in space.

4. Critical Thinking:

a. Why is the Moon a non luminous object?
Moon is also a non-luminous object as it does not have its own light. We see it because it reflects the Sun's light.

b. Ripe fruits fall down from the tree. Why?
The ripe fruit falls down from the tree due to gravity. Gravity is a force that the Earth exerts on objects downwards towards the centre of the Earth.

5. Social Emotional Thinking:

Do you think loud music or loudspeakers should be played at night? Discuss.
Loud music should not be played at night.

- can cause disturbance to neighbors
- others may want to sleep, study, do other things that require concentration
- causes noise pollution

6. Creativity:

Make different shapes with the help of clay. Do you need to apply force? Which effect of force do you observe during this activity?

Worksheets: Answers

Lesson 1 The Beginning of Time

1. a. Intellect and invention, b. Weapons and tools
2. Since many of the tools were made out of stone, the early age was called the 'Stone Age.'
3. a. Early humans learnt to start a fire by rubbing together two stones or sticks.

b. Early humans learnt to ride horses and started using them to move from one place to another.

4. Answers may vary. Accept all appropriate responses.

Lesson 2 Maps and Directions

1. a. Road map, b. Weather map, c. Political map, d. Physical map
2. Cartography
3. a. Weather map, b. Political map, c. Road map
4. Answers may vary. Accept all appropriate responses.

Lesson 3 Continents and Oceans

1. a. Europe, b. South America
2. a. Antarctica, b. Arctic Ocean
3. a. Pacific Ocean, b. Indian Ocean
4. a. Antarctic Ocean is also known as the Southern Ocean.
   b. Atlantic Ocean is S-shaped.
5. Answers may vary. Accept all appropriate responses.

Lesson 4 India—Physical

1. a. False, b. True
2. a. Lakshadweep, b. Port Blair
3. a. Island, b. Coast
4. Answers may vary. Accept all appropriate responses.

Lesson 5 India—Political

1. a. The three levels of government are the central government, the state government and the local government.
   b. The local government works at the village level.
2. a. The state governments are based in the respective state capitals.
   b. The gram panchayat is responsible for the welfare of the village.
3. Telangana
4. Answers may vary. Accept all appropriate responses.

Lesson 6 India—Food and Clothing

1. c.
2. The food served in communal meals comprises the staple food of that region. The temples always serve healthy and nutritious

food. The devotees sit on the floor in lines. The food is usually served on leaf plates. The servers hurry across the lines and serve everyone each item, one-by-one.

3. Answers may vary. Accept all appropriate responses.
4. Langar and dham

Lesson 7 Indian Culture and Traditions

1. a. Bharatnatyam, which means Bharata's dancing, is one of the main classical dance styles of India.
   b. Bharatnatyam was originally performed exclusively by female temple dancers. Public performances of Bharatnatyam began after 1930.
2. A programme of Bharatnatyam usually lasts for two hours without interruption and includes a specific list of procedures, all performed by one dancer.
3. The veena is a musical instrument that is used in both Carnatic and Hindustani music. It has a large resonating gourd under each end of its hollow wooden body.
4. The two main forms of Indian classical music are Carnatic and Hindustani music.
5. Answers may vary. Accept all appropriate responses.

Lesson 8 National Symbols and Emblem

1. a. Tiger – National animal of India, b. Lotus – National flower of India, c. Banyan tree – National tree of India, d. Peacock – National bird of India
2. The symbol of the Indian rupee was adopted by the government of India on 15 July 2010. It is a combination of Devanagari 'Ra' and the Roman capital 'R' with two parallel horizontal stripes running through it at the top. The lines represent the national flag and also the 'equal to' sign.
3. a. – iv., b. – iii., c. – i., d. – v., e. – ii.
4. Answers may vary. Accept all appropriate responses.

Lesson 9 Important Cities of India

New Delhi

1. Qutab Minar is a 73-metre high tower. Qutub-ud-din Aibak laid the foundation of Qutab Minar in 1199. The tower has five storeys. The first three storeys are made of red sandstone, while

the fourth and fifth storeys are made of marble and sandstone. Qutub-ud-din Aibak commenced the construction of Qutab Minar, but could only finish the base. His successor, Iltutmush, added three more storeys, and in 1368, Firoz Shah Tughlak constructed the fifth and the last storey. (Accept any five.)

2. a. True, b. False
3. Answers may vary. Accept all appropriate responses.
4. Answers may vary. Accept all appropriate responses.

Mumbai

1. a. protected, b. forty
2. a. False, b. True
3. Answers may vary. Accept all appropriate responses.
4. Answers may vary. Accept all appropriate responses.

Kolkata

1. c., a., b., d.
2. Vidyasagar Setu, Vivekananda Setu and Nivedita Setu
3. a. Howrah, b. 1965
4. Answers may vary. Accept all appropriate responses.

Chennai

1. The city of Chennai has grown around Fort St George.
2. A major portion of the fort was completed on St George's Day, i.e., 23 April 1640. Hence, it was named Fort St George.
3. St Mary's Church, one of the oldest surviving Anglican churches built by the British in India, was constructed within Fort St George in 1680.
4. The French captured the fort in mid-18th century.

Lesson 10 Living and Non-living Things

1. a. Adaptive, b. Polar bear, c. Camel
2. The polar bear's white-coloured fur helps it hide in the snow when it is in danger.
3. The mountain goat has strong hooves to help it run up the slopes of rocky mountains.
4. Answers may vary. Accept all appropriate responses.

Lesson 11 Parts of a Plant

1. a. Germination, b. Water, c. Warmth, d. Oxygen, e. Light
2. Answers may vary. Accept all appropriate responses.
3. Dwarf willow is the smallest tree in the world. The average size

of the tree is about two inches.

4. Answers may vary. Accept all appropriate responses.

Lesson 12 Animals

1. Identify the following as Herbivore, Carnivore, Omnivore or Frugivore
   a. Lion - Carnivore
   b. Cow - Herbivore
   c. Bear - Omnivore
   d. Bat - Frugivore
   e. Parrot - Frugivore
   f. Deer – Herbivore
2. Choose the correct option to fill in the blanks.
   a. Producers
   b. Omnivores
   c. Snake
   d. Gills
   e. Amphibians
3. 1) Mammals have fur or hair on their bodies, birds have feathers covering their bodies. 2) Mammals give birth to live young, birds lay eggs from which their young hatch
4. Birds breathe through lungs and Insects breathe through a system of tiny tubes called tracheae.
5. Ostrich & Penguin

Lesson 13 Birds

1. a. forty, b. webbed
2. a. True, b. False, c. False
3. Answers may vary. Accept all appropriate responses.
4. weaver bird-a, woodpecker -d, tailor bird – b, penguin -c

Lesson 14 The Human Body

1. a. The nervous system consists of the brain, spinal cord and nerves.
   b. The brain is divided into two parts – the left and right parts.
2. The vertebral column protects the spinal cord.
3. The kidneys separate the toxins and other waste material from the blood and flush them out.

4. Answers may vary. Accept all appropriate responses.
5. Answers may vary. Accept all appropriate responses.

Lesson 15 The Universe and the Solar System

1. The solar system is made up of the sun, the eight planets and their satellites.
2. a. False, b. True, c. True
3. a. 150, b. 99
4. Answers may vary. Accept all appropriate responses.

Lesson 16 The Earth

1. a. Crust, b. Mantle
2. The inner core of the earth is solid because of the immense pressure exerted by the outer layers.
3. a. Atmosphere, b. Global warming, c. Ozone layer
4. Answers may vary. Accept all appropriate responses.

Lesson 17 Natural Resources

1. When flowing water drops abruptly and vertically from a height, it's called a waterfall. When a large volume of water is involved, the waterfall is called a cataract. Waterfalls of small height and less steepness are called cascades. One of the most famous waterfalls in the world, the Niagara Falls, forms part of the boundary between the United States of America and Canada. A large part of the great river above the falls is diverted for hydroelectric power generation.
2. a. Goat, b. American
3. Answers may vary. Accept all appropriate responses.
4. Answers may vary. Accept all appropriate responses.

Lesson 18 Matter and Its Properties

1. a. Any substance that has mass and occupies space is known as matter.
   b. The liquid state is one of the three states of matter. The molecules in liquids can move around slightly. Hence, liquids flow and take the shape of the container.
   c. A molecule is the smallest independent part of a substance that has all the properties of that substance.

2. a. The molecules of gases are spread out in an open space freely. The molecules are always moving. Hence, gases take the shape of the container and fill up all the space inside a container.
   b. Matter is made up of tiny particles called atoms.
3. The arrangement of molecules in matter determines the state of the matter.
4. Answers may vary. Accept all appropriate responses.

Lesson 19 Energy and Forces

1. a. False, b. True
2. Newton realised that there must be a force pulling the apple from the tree to the ground.
3. Circle: Mercury, Mars, Saturn Underline: Jupiter, Neptune
4. Answers may vary. Accept all appropriate responses.